Printed and Published in Great Britain by D. C. THOMSON & CO., LTD.,
185 Fleet Street, London, EC4A 2HS.
© D. C. THOMSON & CO., LTD., 2002.
ISBN 0 85116 816 7

NOT LIKELY!

WELL, I DON'T LIKE IT. TIDY IT!

ATOES

A MENACE DOESN'T TIDY ROOMS. A MENACE ESCAPES!

GRR! I'LL TELL YOUR DADDY, LADDY!

LEAP!

So —

I'VE A FEW JOBS TO DO . . .

. . . BEFORE I MAKE DENNIS TIDY HIS ROOM.

WHAP!

Later —

SHOULD BE SAFE TO COME HOME NOW.

NO, IT'S NOT! YOU'RE GOING TO TIDY YOUR ROOM!

SLAM

THAT'S WHAT YOU THINK . . .

. . . I'LL ESCAPE THROUGH THE LOOSE BOARD IN THE FENCE.

THOUGHT YOU MIGHT.

SO I NAILED IT UP! THERE'S NO ESCAPE.

WHUMP!

GNOUCH.

YES THERE IS. UP THE TREE!

THAT WOULD WORK.

IF I HADN'T GREASED THE TREE. THERE'S NO ESCAPE FROM TIDYING YOUR ROOM.

YES, THERE IS . . .

FLATTEN

GRRR! FOILED!

. . . LOOK — THERE ISN'T ENOUGH SPACE LEFT IN THIS STORY!

REACH FOR THE STARS
with DENNIS and GNASHER
THIS WAY UP
PLEASE CLOSE THE DOOR
GNASHEY!
WAHEY! I KNEW THE SPACEMAN WOULDN'T NOTICE US ADDING THIS SIDECAR!
ZOOM!

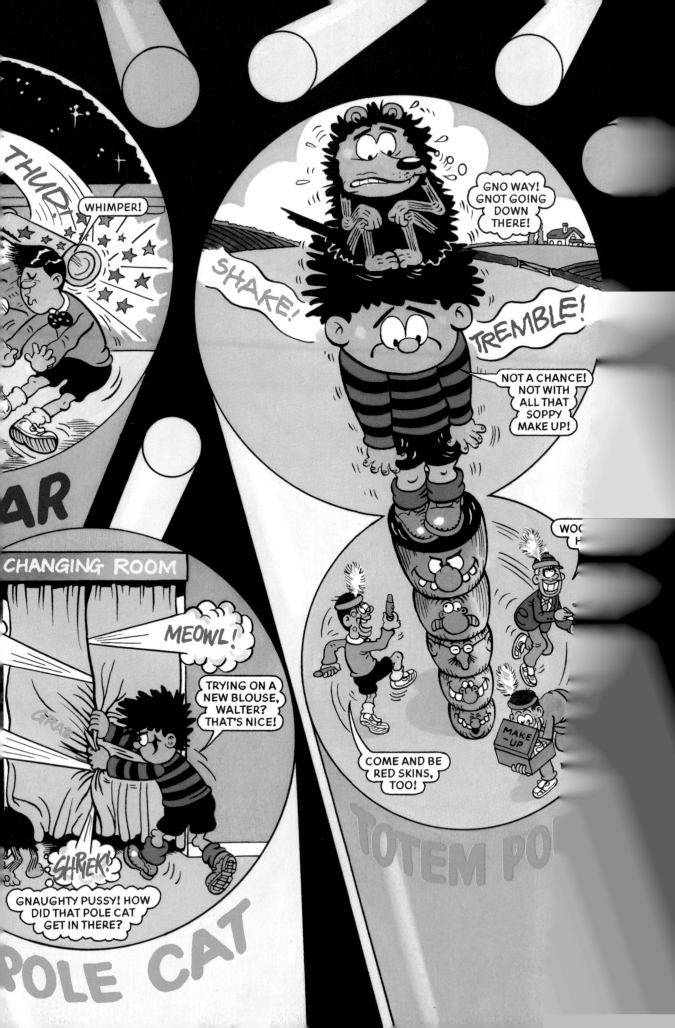

Inviting Disaster!

MY BOSS IS INVITING US TO DINNER!

HOW NICE!

A-AND HE WANTS US TO BRING D-DENNIS AND HIS PETS!

RIP!

DAD'S BOSS DOESN'T KNOW ME!

WHAT'S BITING YOU?

OOOOO! LET ME TELL YOU!

SUDDENLY FIND YOURSELF DANCING?

IT'S OKAY! YOU'VE BEEN BITTEN BY FLEAS!

GSORRY! THINK THEY'RE GMINE!

GOT A PAIN IN THE NECK?

S'OKAY! YOU'VE BEEN BITTEN BY A VAMPIRE!

GNAFF OFF!

SUDDENLY GONE DARK? NOT OKAY!

IT MEANS YOU'VE BEEN BITTEN BY A SHARK!

HELP! LET ME OUT!

GNOTHING WE CAN DO!

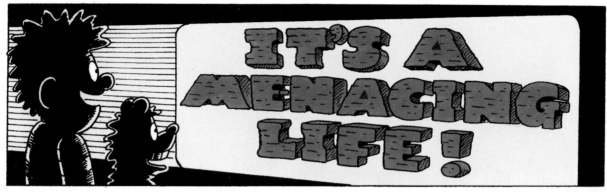

HUH! EVEN THE DRIVER'S LEFT—I'M GOING NOWHERE ON THIS!

HOW BRAVE! I PASSED A SNAIL!

STILL! THERE'S ALWAYS A PLACE FOR THE MENACE!

HI, WALTER!

THE MENACE!

BYE, WALTER—I'M OFF TO THE CINEMA!

WHIMPER!

ZOOM!

AT THE LOCAL CINEMA—

ZOOM!

SHOWING TODAY
BOUNDS OF THE BASKETBALL

Q HERE

A BIG QUEUE, BUT THERE'S ALWAYS A PLACE FOR THE MENACE!

TAP!

ER—HAVE MY PLACE!

DON'T WANT THE MENACE STANDING BEHIND ME!

TODAY
5 OF THE
TBALL

CINEMA

ROOM FOR ONE!

SEE...

GNASHER'S HIDING IN DENNIS'S JERSEY!

... THERE'S ALWAYS A PLACE FOR THE MENACE!

ULP!

AND THIS IS IT!

GROAN! KEPT IN FOR ANOTHER WEEK!

DENNIS'S BED ROOM

PUSH!

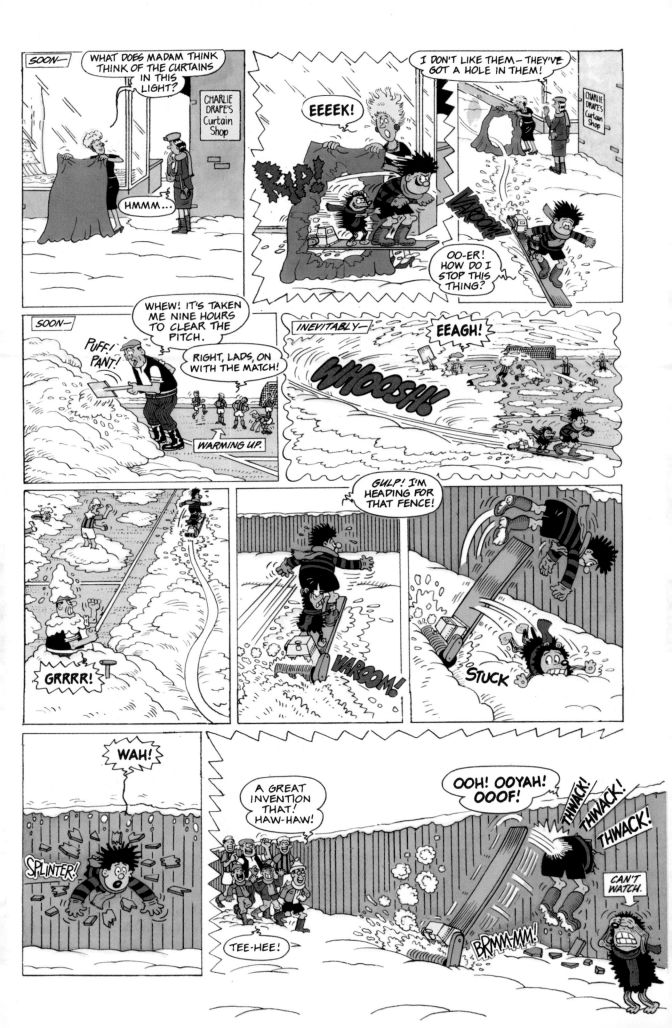

FAIRY CAKES! SPIFFING!

GINGERBREAD BABIES! SWEET!

ICING

WELL, LET THEM BAKE! FOR 4 HOURS AT 160 DEGREES — IN A SAUNA!

SAUNA

BOOT!

OF COURSE, SOFTY BOYS LIKE TO EAT.

CLOSED DUE TO HORRIBLE FOOD AND ROTTEN SMELLS

CELERY 'N' CRISPBREAD AN' OTHER SOPPY STUFF!

TODAY'S CHOICE: TAKE IT OR LEAVE IT!

MMM! MY MOUTH-WATERING SPECIALITY. SAGO AND CABBAGE CUSTARD.

MAYBE WE'LL GIVE SOME TO THE SOFTIES.

TA, DEN!

The crash wakens Walter at last!

EEK! WHAT WAS THAT? I DO HATE TO HEAR KITCHEN IMPLEMENTS BEING ABUSED!

IT'S BEEN AN EDUKASHUN!

WORSE THAN THAT, WALTER, O PRINCE OF SOFTNESS! DENNIS HAS BEEN TEACHING MENACING!

YES! NOW LOTS OF MENACES WILL TRY TO STOP OUR SOFT WAYS!

DISGRACEFUL! AND IN BASH STREET SCHOOL, A SHRINE TO KNOWLEDGE!